Love My Friends!

21366 Disney Junior 400 Page Coloring Book

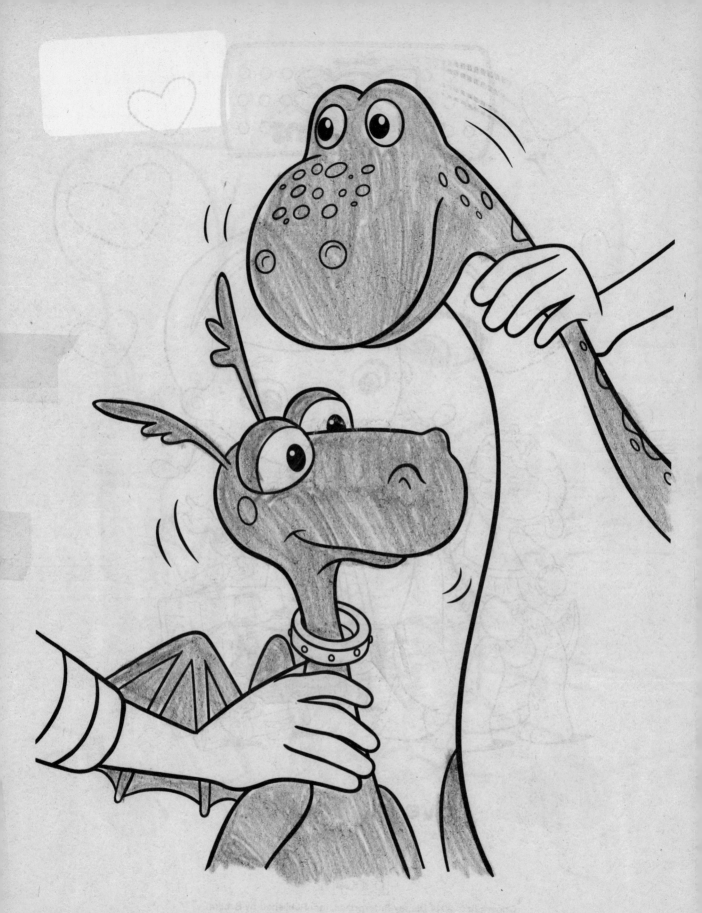

Doc and Donny are playing with their stuffed animals.
"Roar!" says Bronty.

"Ah!" says Doc. "Run away, Stuffy!"

"Doc! Donny!" calls Dad. "Time for lunch."

"My salami sandwich is great, Dad," says Donny.

"Here, Bronty," says Donny. "Have some salami!"

"Finish up, Donny," says Mom.
"I'll take you to soccer practice."

Circle the items that begin with the letter B.

8

"We'll be in the backyard, Dad!" says Doc.

"This is fun," says Lambie. "Let's go, Bronty!"

"Hey, Lenny," says Bronty.

"Sorry," says Lenny. "I have to go!"

"I wonder why Lenny ran away," says Lambie.

"I don't know!" says Bronty, breathing on Lambie.

"Bronty, your breath is smelly!" says Lambie.

"Time for a checkup!" says Doc.

"But I feel fine," says Bronty.

"You have bad breath, Bronty," says Hallie.

"I'm going to give you a dental checkup," says Doc.

"Open wide!"

"You have a piece of salami stuck in your teeth," says Doc.

21

© Disney

"You have stinkysalamibreath!" says Doc.

"Let's add that to the Big Book of Boo Boos!"

"We can treat this with a toothbrush and toothpaste!"

"That didn't hurt a bit!" says Bronty.

"Your breath is minty-fresh, Bronty!" says Lenny.
"Let's play!"

"Thanks, Doc!"

Doc and her friend Henry are ready
to watch a meteor shower.

"Anyone want a star cookie?" asks Dad.

Henry has a new telescope.

"What do you see?" asks Doc. "A star?
Two stars? A whole galaxy?"

"I can't see a thing!" says Henry. "Everything is fuzzy."

"I'll see if I can fix it," says Doc.

"Better hurry," says Dad.
"The meteor shower will start soon!"

"Hi, Hallie," says Doc.
"Meet Aurora, our new patient!"

"This place is great," says Aurora.

"Oh, sorry!" says Aurora. "Didn't see you there."

"Nice doggie!" says Aurora.

"You need an eye exam," says Doc.

"Tell me what you see on this eye chart," says Doc.

"Pretzels!" says Aurora.

"I have a diagnosis!" shouts Doc.
"Aurora has Blurrystaritis!"

"Can you help her see better?" asks Lambie.

"Doctors give kids—and hippos—
glasses to help them see," says Doc.

"I'll say!"

"I think I see the problem!" says Doc.
"Your eyepiece is missing!"

"I wonder what happened to it," says Lambie.

"Here it is!" says Stuffy. "I found it!"

"This eyepiece will help you see clearly," says Doc.

"Everything is so clear!" says Aurora. "And close!"

"I fixed the telescope!" says Doc.
"Just in time!" says Dad.

"The meteor shower is happening!" shouts Henry.
"Thanks, Doc!"

"Look at my new ring!"

How sparkly!

Way to go!

Super cute!

"Now, where am I?"

Butterflies look like bows.

Oops!

Farmer Mickey

Fabulous Fruits

Yummy Veggies

I'm starry-eyed.

Geared up to go!

© Disney

HOP LIKE A FROG!

"I can hop with the best of them!"

Bath Time

The bubbles are everywhere!

Let it Slide!

Let's do something goofy.

All dolled up!

You're number one!

Which piece completes the picture?

A

B

C

Your Answer:

Answer: A

Your Answer: A & D

Answer: A, D

How lovely!

Pluto loves shapes.

Pete

What's your favorite color?

How many tools do you count?

Your Answer:

Use the grid to draw Daisy.

Which line leads to Mickey?

Your Answer: 1

Oh, Pickle Juice!

Together is better.

Let's get to work.

The race is on!

Use the grid to draw Mickey.

Cross out any letter that appears FIVE or more times in the grid.
Write the remaining letters in order on the lines below to reveal the message.

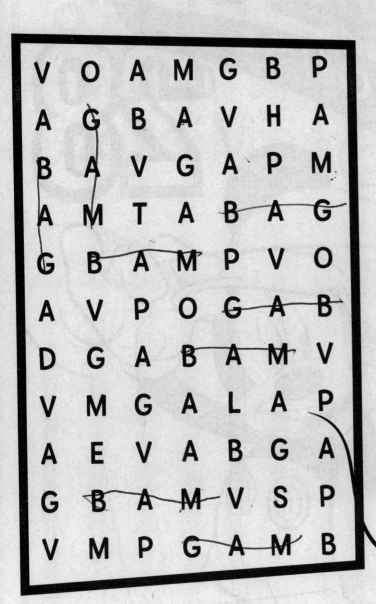

V	O	A	M	G	B	P
A	G	B	A	V	H	A
B	A	V	G	A	P	M
A	M	T	A	B	A	G
G	B	A	M	P	V	O
A	V	P	O	G	A	B
D	G	A	B	A	M	V
V	M	G	A	L	A	P
A	E	V	A	B	G	A
G	B	A	M	V	S	P
V	M	P	G	A	M	B

————— —————,

————— ————— ————— —————

"See ya!"

What a special way . . .

. . . to spend the day!

© Disney

Scooter Girl

Ready to soar!

I want you!

I'm ready to roll!

"A pretty bow for me!"

Tweet-tweet-tweet!

Friendship warms the heart.

© Disney

"Hello, friends! ¡Hola, amigos!"

"Let's go, tools!"

Who is a bright helper?
Connect the dots to find out.

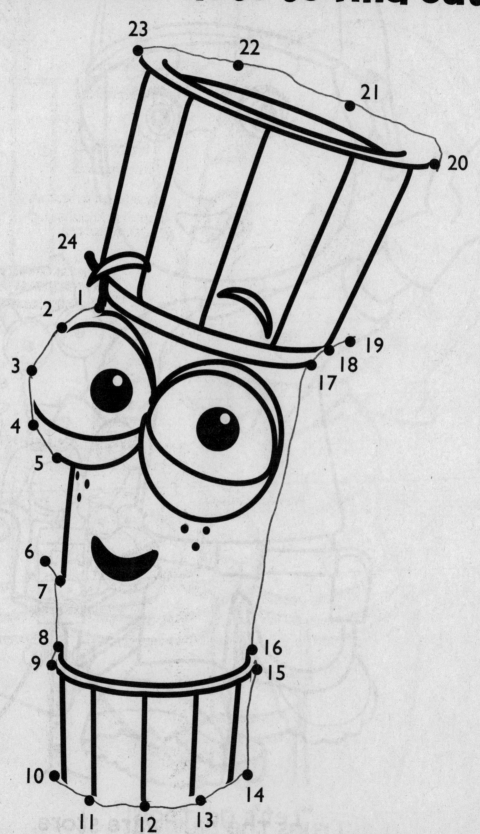

Kelly runs the hardware store.

With the right tools...

... Manny can fix anything!

© Disney

DRAW HANDY MANNY.

Use the grid to draw Manny.

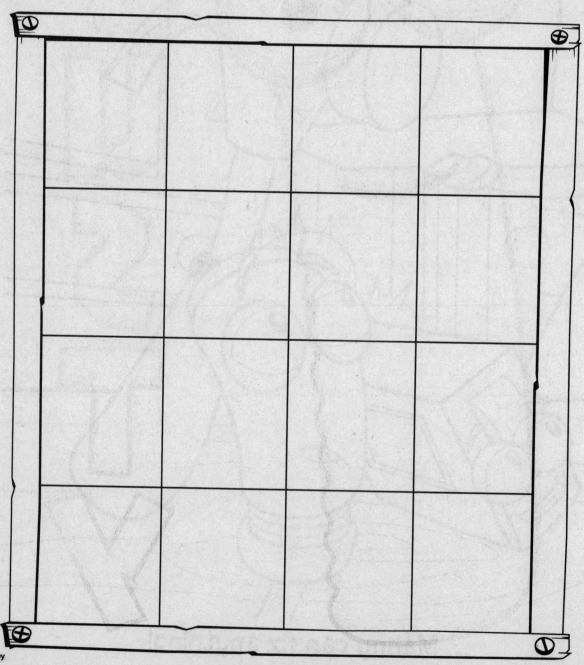

113

Meet Stretch, Pat, Dusty, Felipe, Turner, Rusty, and Squeeze.

"We've got a big job to do,"
says Manny Garcia.

© Disney

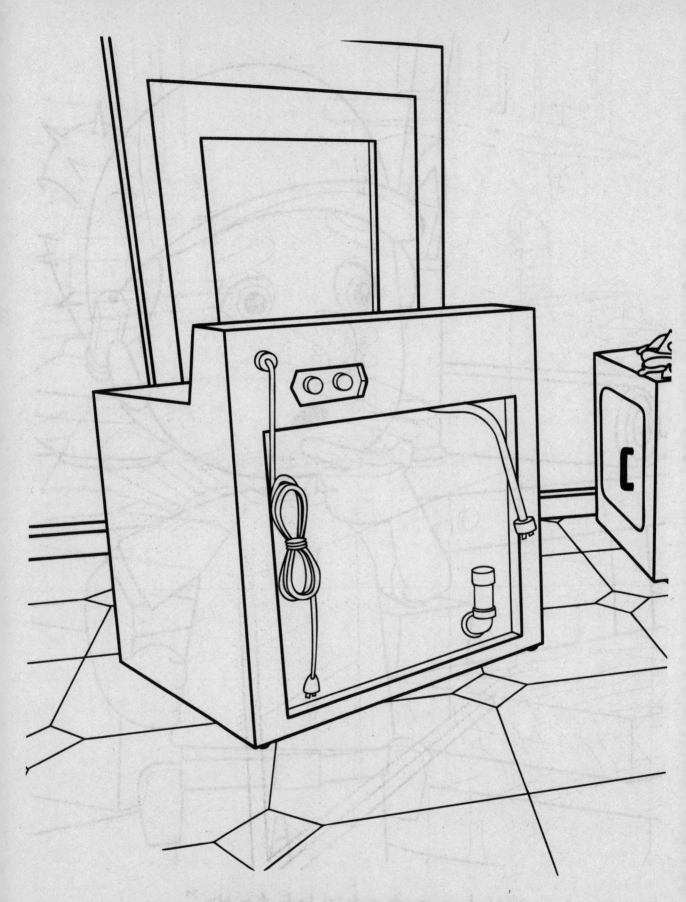

This looks like a job...

...for Handy Manny!

WHO AM I?

A. PAT

C. FLICKER

B. DUSTY

D. MANNY

Answer: A

WHICH FELIPE IS DIFFERENT?

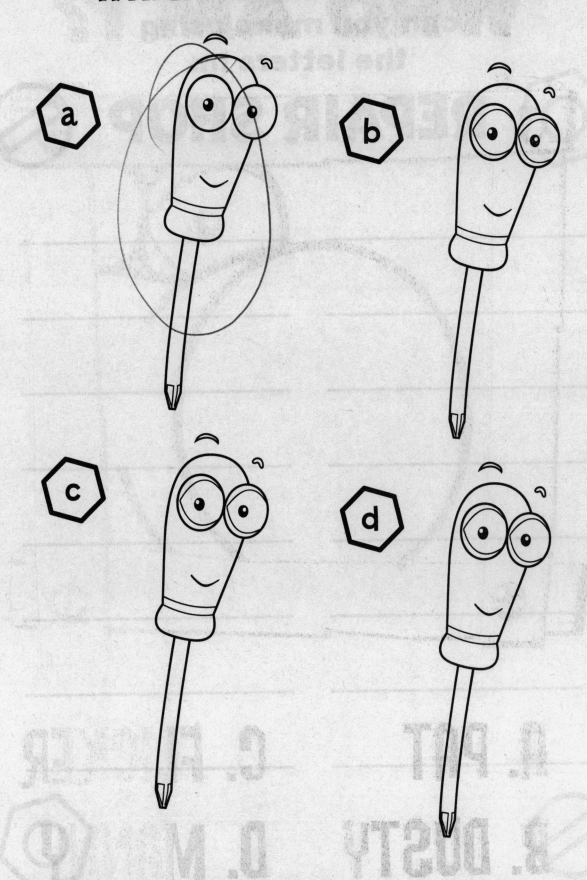

119

How many words
can you make using
the letters in:
REPAIR SHOP

_____   _____

_____   _____

_____   _____

_____   _____

_____   _____

_____   _____

_____   _____

PAT

"Let's get to work!!"

"¡Muy rápido!"

"¡Sí vamanos! Let's go!"

"There's no leak we can't fix!"

"There's no task we can't do!"

WHICH TWO PICTURES ARE THE SAME?

Answers: A and D

128

"Uh-oh!"

© Disney

Help Handy Manny to the toolbox!

Start

Finish

Mr. Lopart runs a candy store.

STRETCH

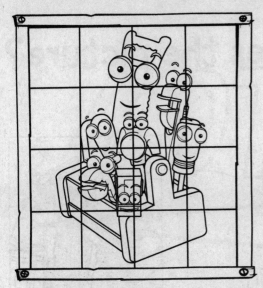

DRAW THE TOOLS.

Use the grid to draw the tools.

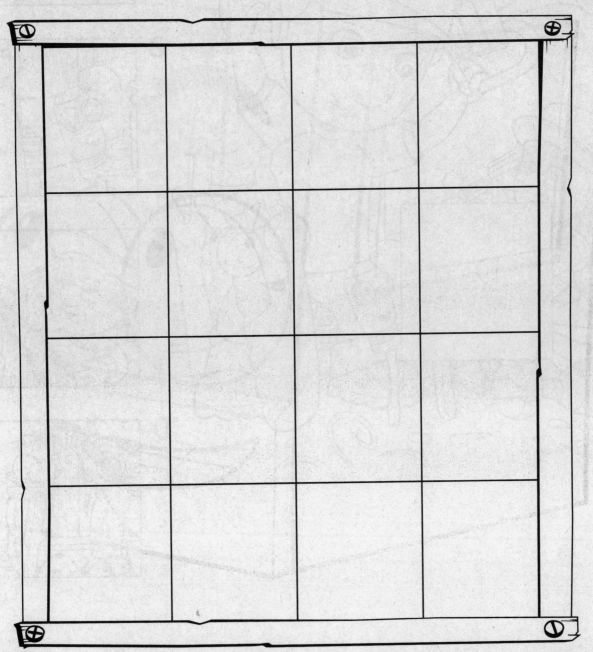

Which piece completes the picture?

"Hello, Fix-It!"

"Hola, Señora Portillo.
We're here to fix your stove."

"Oh, thank you! ¡Gracias!"

Squeeze knows how to apply herself.

Help Dusty to the other tools!

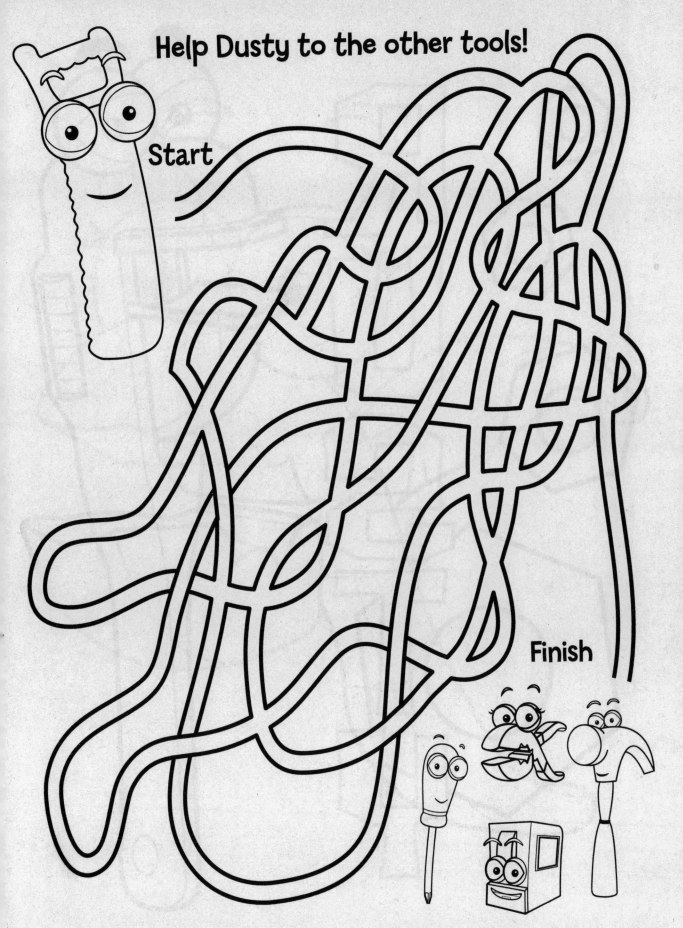

Start

Finish

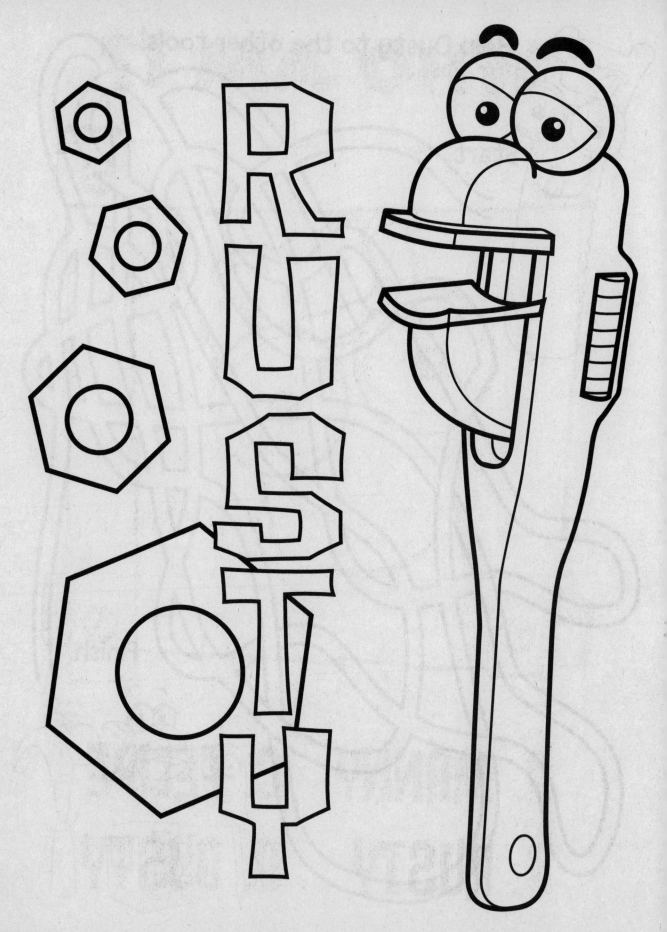

WHO AM I?

A. MANNY   C. FELIPE

B. RUSTY   D. DUSTY

Answer: D.

The handy repairman . . .

. . . shops at Kelly's Handy Hardware store.

© Disney

x

z

145

FRIENDS THINK BETTER TOGETHER!
WHICH LINE WILL LEAD TO
THE CORRECT TOOL TO HELP WITH THE LEAK?

Answer: B

It's a Snap!

"Hello, friends! ¡Hola, amigos!"

Match each Handy Manny to the correct shadow.

Fluffy is loose!

"Oh, oh, oh! This is NOT very safe!"

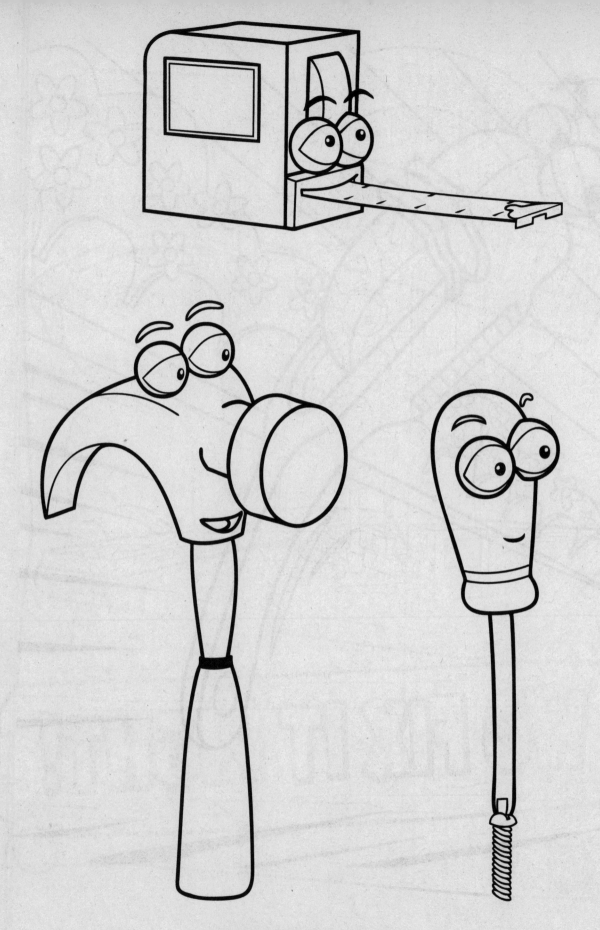

Ready to work.

Manny's hardware store.

Always organized!

Safety first!

Tic-Tac-Toe

WHO AM I?

A. PAT   C. FIX-IT

B. DUSTY   D. STRETCH

"We can do it!"

Manny's front door

Fix-it time!

Fiesta time!

WHICH LINE WILL LEAD TO MR. LOPART?

Answer: A

WHICH MRS. PORTILLO IS DIFFERENT?

Answer: D

© Disney

"There's nothing I can't turn!"

Squeeze is ready!

© Disney

Find 6 things that are different in the picture below.

Answers: 1 and 2 on the ruler, tool box is missing a bolt, stripe in Manny's hat, the O in Hola, the pencil behind Manny's ear, Pat's smile, Stretch's eyebrows

"Let's go, tools!"

The gang's all here!

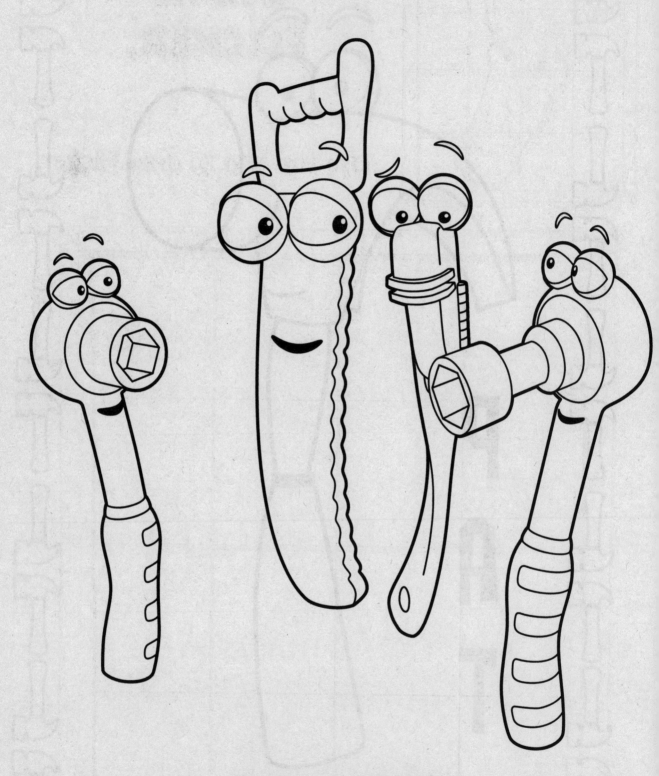

Dusty and Rusty
meet Totts and Ticks.

DRAW FLICKER.

Use the grid to draw Flicker.

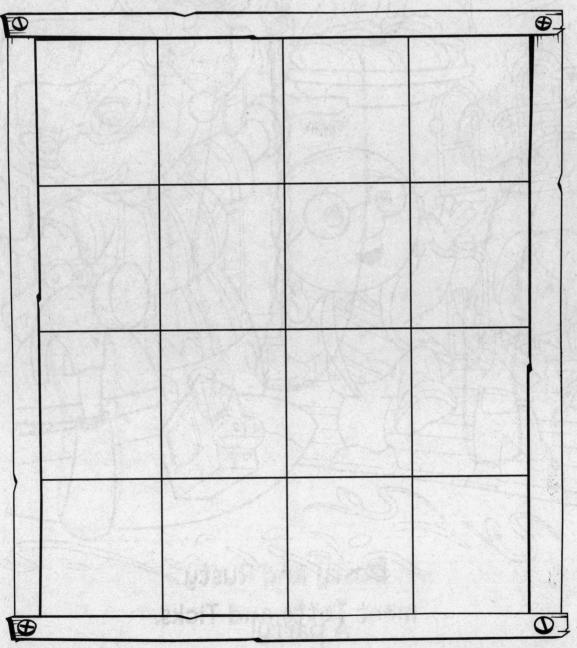

© Disney

A party!

¡La fiesta!

WHO AM I?

A. RUSTY   **C. PAT**

B. FELIPE   **D. FIX-IT**

Answer: A

On our way!

"Don't worry, everyone.

We can do the job."

© Disney

¡Adiós!

It's a snap!

"One small part can make a big difference."

Who is Manny's helper?
Connect the dots to find out.

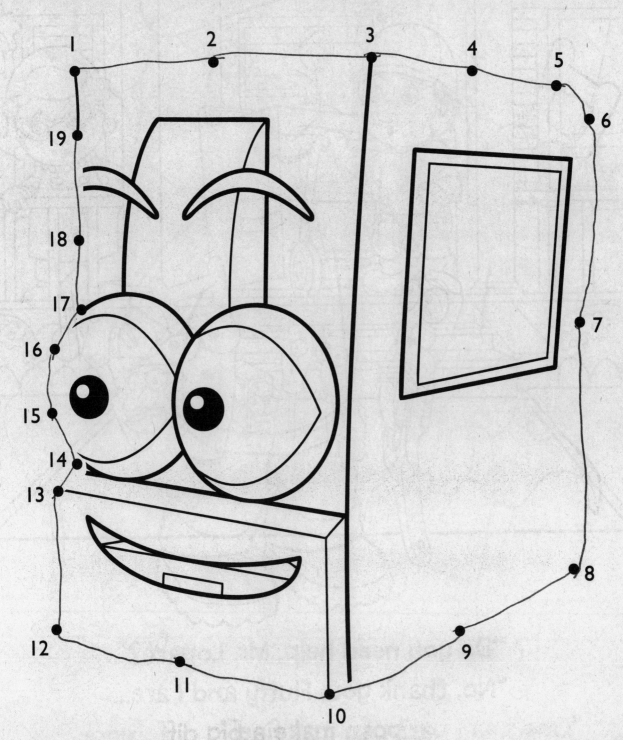

© Disney

"Do you need help, Mr. Lopart?"
"No, thank you. Fluffy and I are...
oof... just fine!"

It's a
Big Job!

How many words can you make using the letters in:

Friends think best together

_____ _____

_____ _____

_____ _____

_____ _____

_____ _____

_____ _____

_____ _____

_____ _____

_____ _____

_____ _____

"Hola, Manny."

"¡Hola!"

"We can do it.

But I need your help!"

© Disney

WHO AM I?

A. STRETCH   C. FELIPE

B. SQUEEZE   D. TURNER

Fix-It

Mr. Lopart

Match each tool to its shadow.

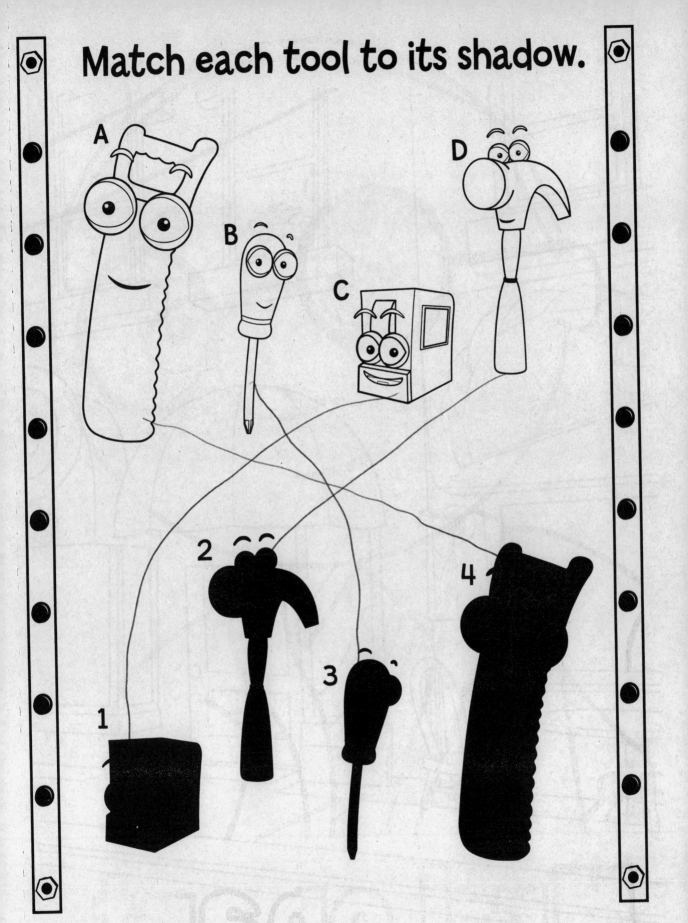

Answers: A-4, B-3, C-1, D-2

Manny's Town

Which piece completes the picture?

WHO AM I?

A. MANNY   C. TURNER

B. MR. LOPART   D. RUSTY

Measure twice.

Cut once.

© Disney

WHICH HANDY MANNY IS DIFFERENT?

Answer: B

202

LOOK UP, DOWN, ACROSS, AND DIAGONALLY FOR THESE WORDS.

PAT
FELIPE
DUSTY
RUSTY

STRETCH
TURNER
SQUEEZE
MANNY

HOLA
FRIEND
LOPART
JOB

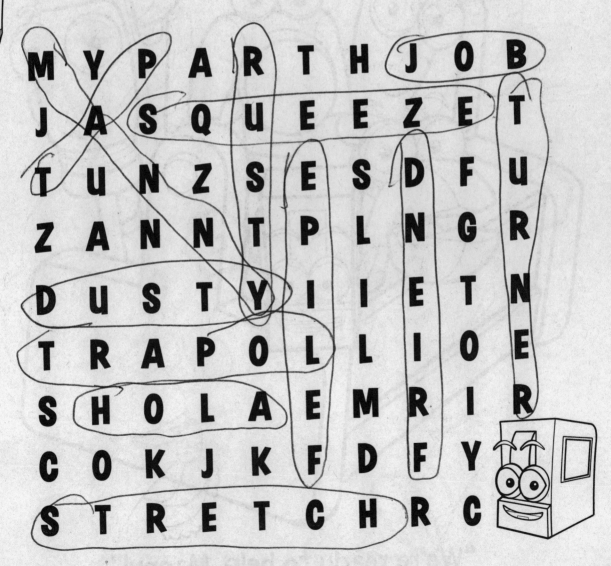

```
M Y P A R T H J O B
J A S Q U E E Z E T
T U N Z S E S D F U
Z A N N T P L N G R
D U S T Y I I E T N
T R A P O L L I O E
S H O L A E M R I R
C O K J K F D F Y
S T R E T C H R C
```

© Disney

"We're ready to help, Manny!"

Match each tool to its shadow.

Answers: A-2, B-3, C-1

Friends think best together.

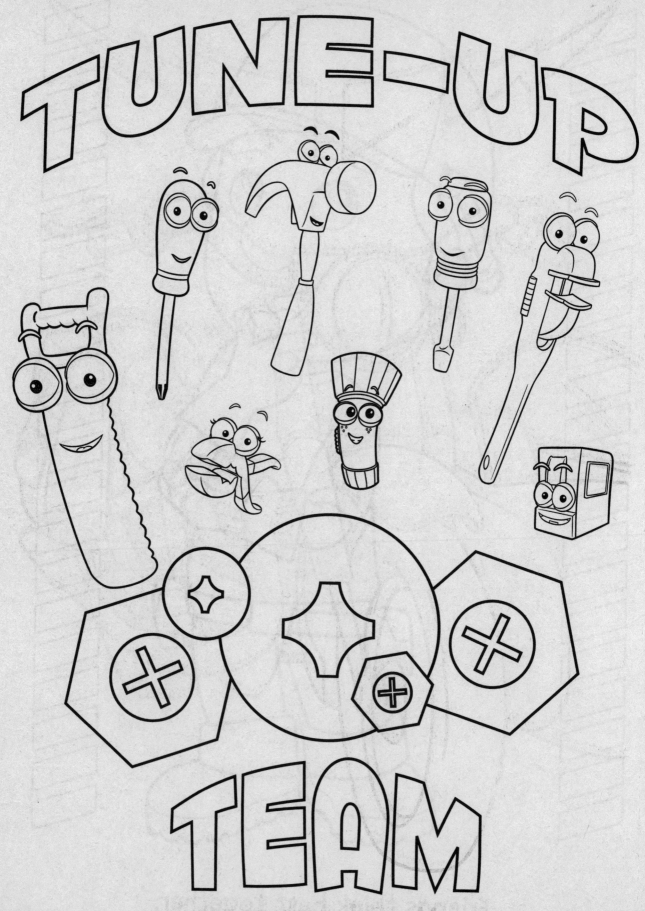

Manny's motorcycle

Match each neighbor to the shadow.

Answer: A-3, B-1, C-2

Which piece completes the picture?

A

B

C

D

Your
Answer: A

Answer: A

© Disney

Flicker "lightens" Felipe's job.

"¡Gracias, Flicker!"

"Ready to work?"

"Let's get rollin'!"

Rollin' right up!

"¡Muy bueno! Very good!"

Tic-Tac-Toe

Spinner meets Turner.

"Great job, everyone!"

One Big Crew

Hard at Work

DRAW STRETCH.

Use the grid to draw Stretch.

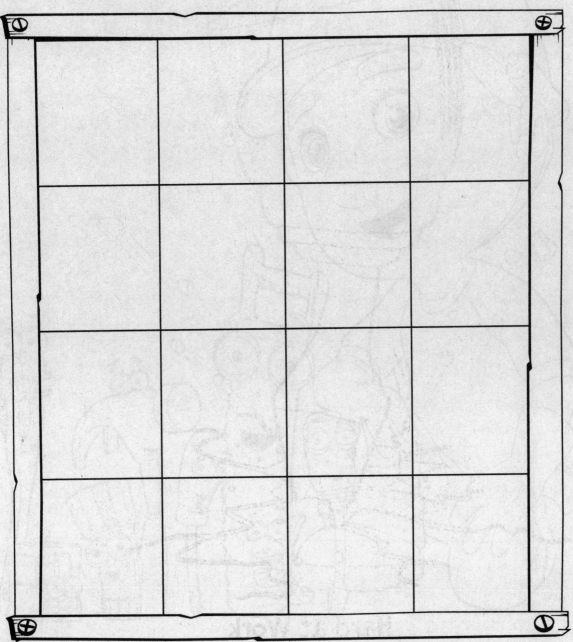

TOOL TEAM

Ready to Ride

POWER CREW

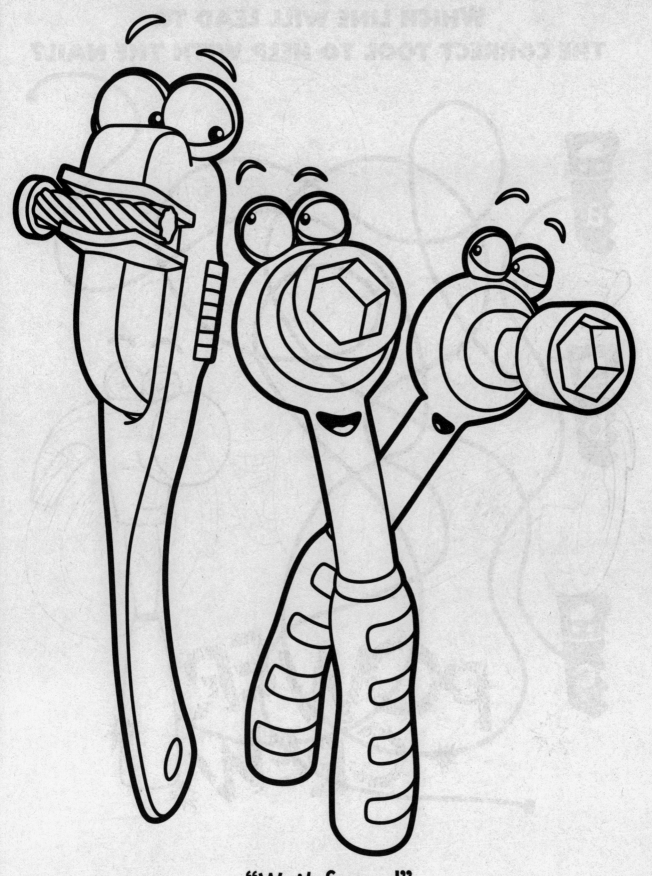

"Wait for us!"

FRIENDS THINK BETTER TOGETHER!
WHICH LINE WILL LEAD TO
THE CORRECT TOOL TO HELP WITH THE NAIL?

Answer: B

Roland keeps things organized.

"Hola, Junior."

The right tools for the job!

"We're one handy crew!"

Time to clean up this place.

Which piece completes the picture?

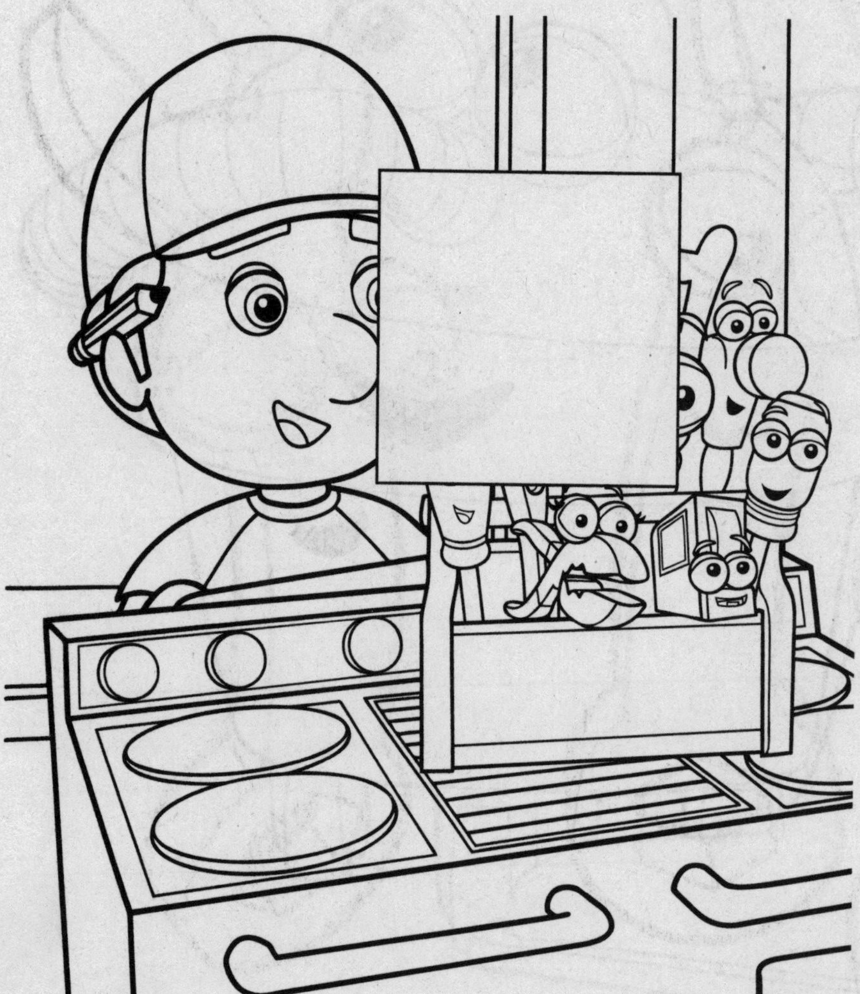

A

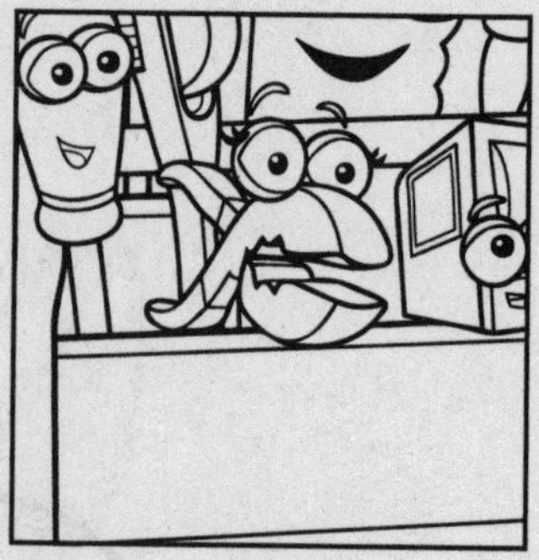

B

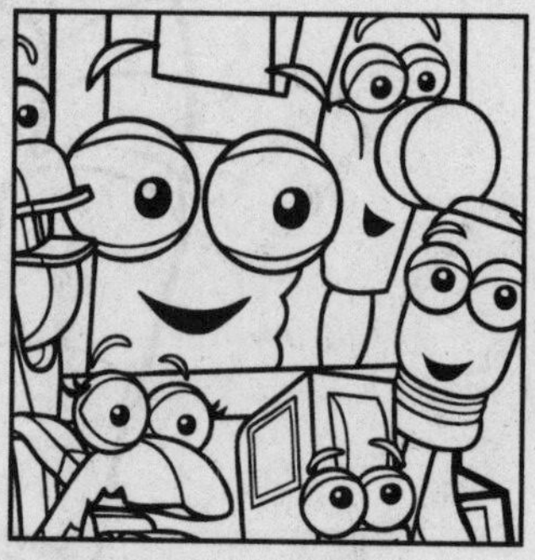

C

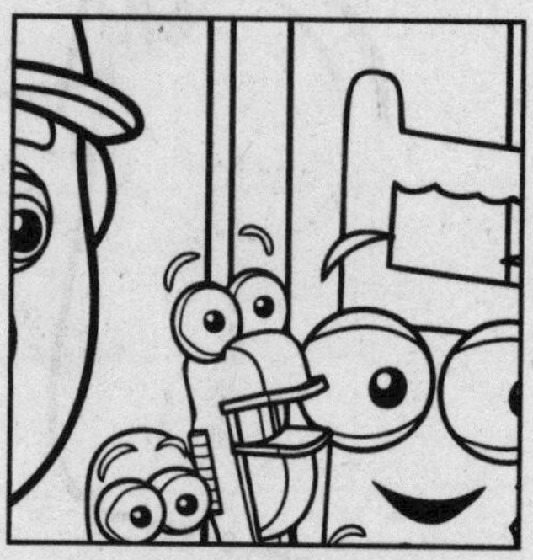

D

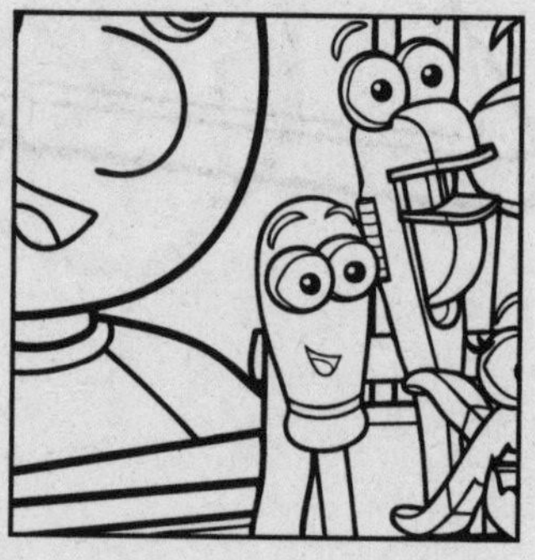

Your Answer: C

Meet Junior, Lefty, and Lily.

WHICH TURNER IS DIFFERENT?

Answer: C

How many words can you make using the letters in:

Safety First

_____   _____

_____   _____

_____   _____

_____   _____

_____   _____

_____   _____

_____   _____

_____   _____

_____   _____

Let's fix it!

WHO AM I?

A. MANNY   C. KELLY

B. FLUFFY   D. SQUEEZE

Answer: C

239

SQUEEZE

WHICH LINE WILL LEAD TO FLICKER?

241

DRAW KELLY.

Use the grid to draw Kelly.

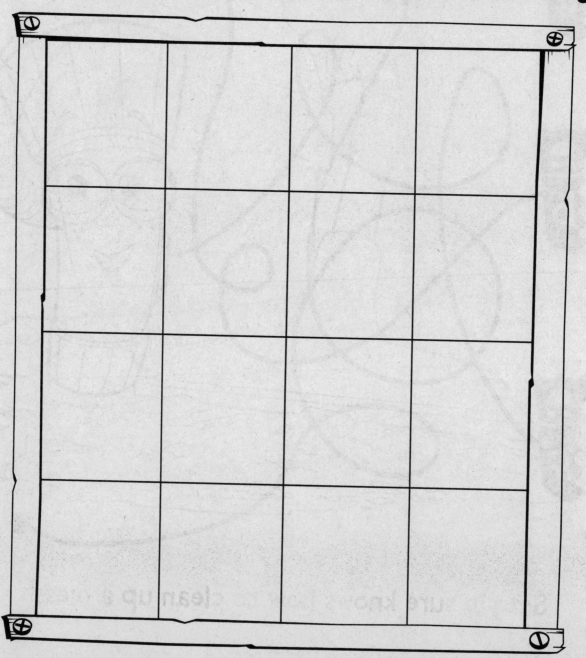

Sneeze sure knows how to clean up a mess!

WHICH SQUEEZE IS DIFFERENT?

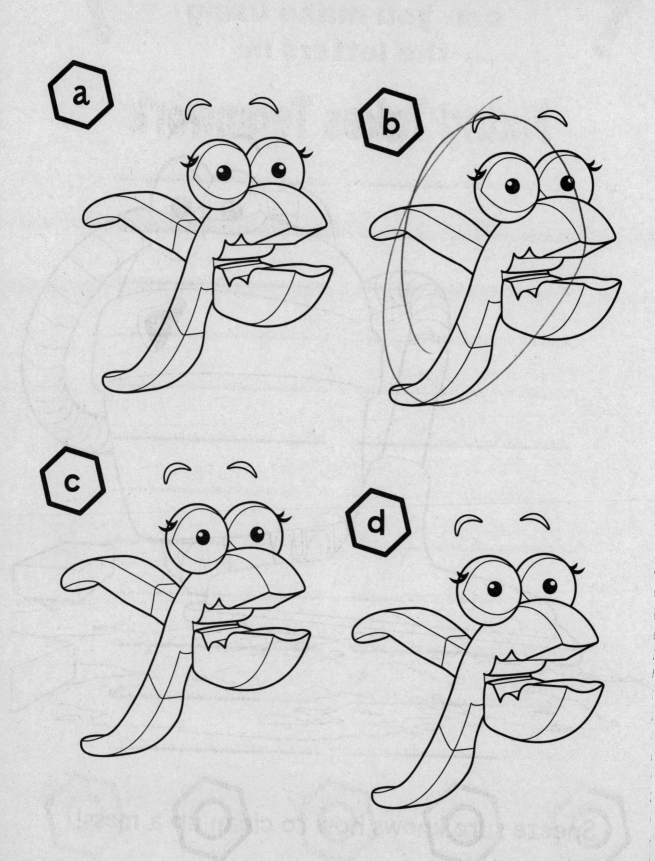

Answer: B

How many words can you make using the letters in:

Fixing Takes Teamwork

_____   _____

_____   _____

_____   _____

_____   _____

_____   _____

_____   _____

_____   _____

_____   _____

_____   _____

_____   _____

Handy Manny and Stretch work together.

Good Job

Lunch Maker

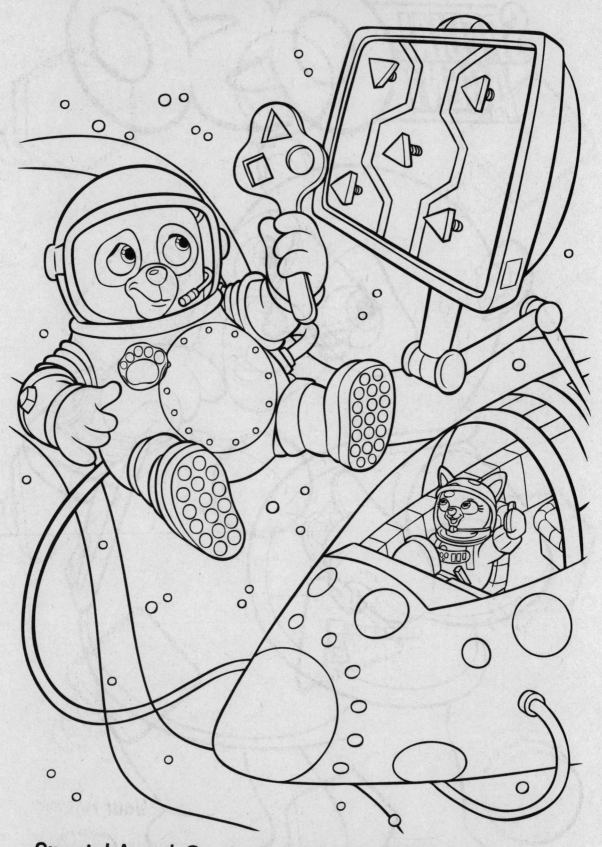

Special Agent Oso is doing Space Repair Training.
He's learning how to fix things in outer space.

How many bolts do you count?

Your Answer:

13

Agent Dotty to Agent Oso!
Use the wrench to tighten the bolts
on the training panel.

Match the wrench to the bolt.
Draw lines to connect the shapes.

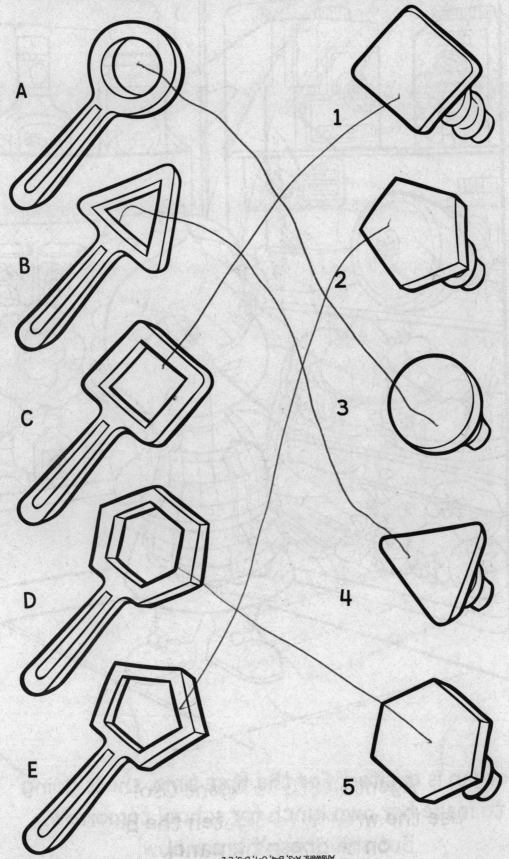

Answers: A-3, B-4, C-1, D-5, E-2

Morgan is excited. For the first time, she is going
to make her own lunch for school tomorrow.
But she doesn't know how!

Circle the food that doesn't belong.

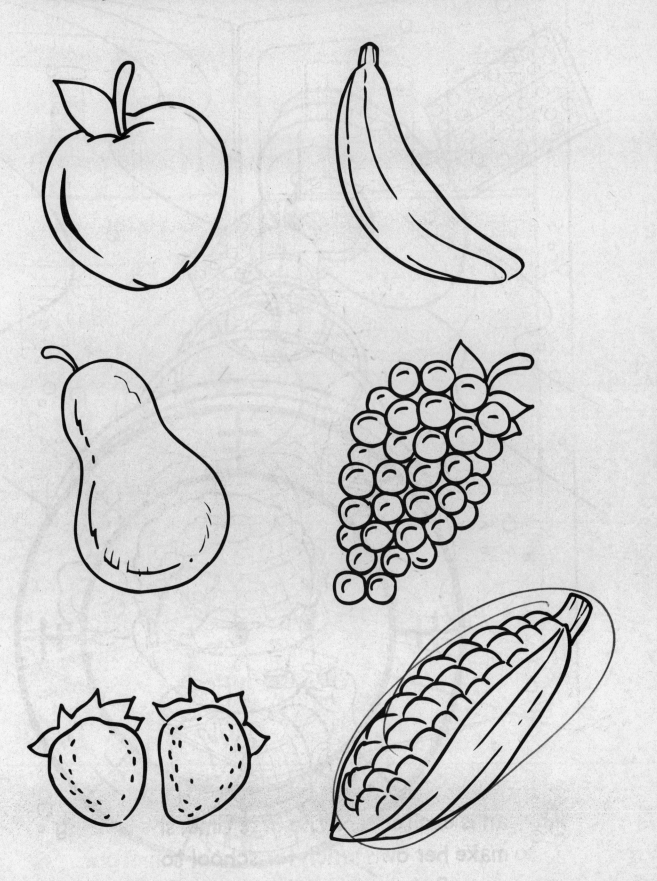

Answer: corn

Special Alert! Morgan needs help
making her first lunch!

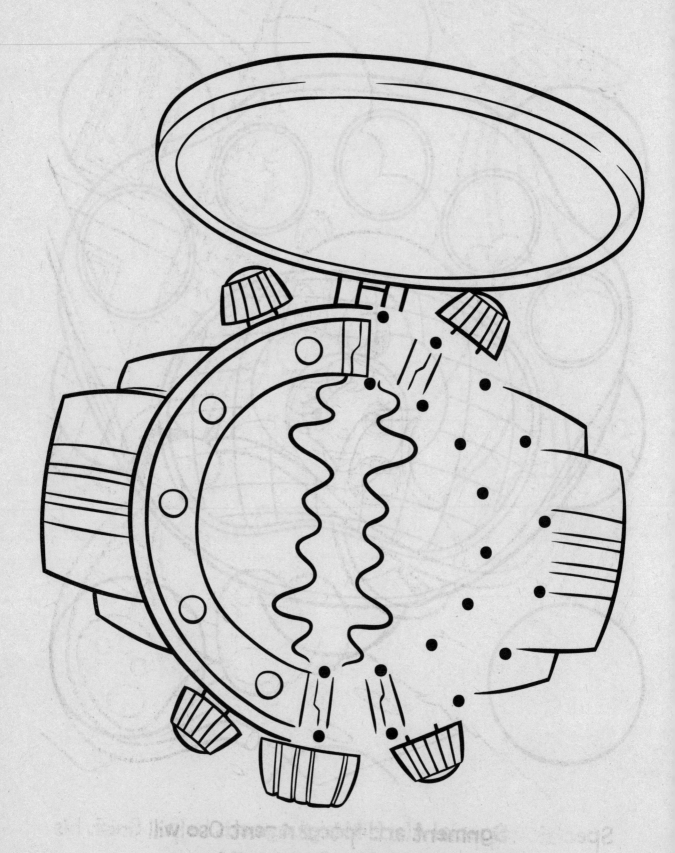

Mister Dos, here. Hurry, Agent Oso!

Special Assignment accepted! Agent Oso will finish his
Space Repair Training later.

Circle the rocket that is different.

I'm so glad you're here, Agent Oso. I have to pack my lunch and put it in the refrigerator before bedtime.

© Disney

Use the code to figure out the 3 special steps.

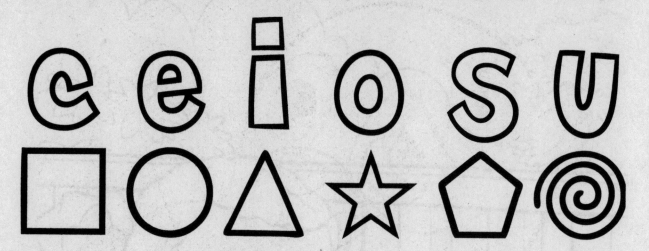

1. Make a l <u>i</u> △ <u>s</u> ⬠ t.

2. Go to the <u>s</u> ⬠ t <u>o</u> ☆ r <u>e</u> ○.

3. Pack your l <u>u</u> ◎ n <u>c</u> ▢ h.

Answers: 1. Make a list. 2. Go to the store. 3. Pack your lunch.

262

Step 1 is to make a list of what we need to pack a lunch.
We may need some expert help.

© Disney

I did it, Agent Oso! My dad helped me make a list of what I want in my lunch. Step 1 is complete!

turkey
cheese
bread
orange
pretzels

Unscramble the words on Morgan's list.

◯ ◯ ◯ ◯ ◯ ◯ ◯ ◯

ruTeyk — TURKEY

seehCe — CHEESE

derBa — BREAD

eaOgrn — ORANGE

rtzlseeP — PRETZELS

Morgan's dad brought her and Agent Oso to the store.
That's step number 2.

Help Agent Oso
and Morgan
find their way
through the store.

End

© Disney

Agent Oso helps make lunch. What a mess!

Morgan made a terrific sandwich. Yum!

Circle items that might be packed in a school lunch.

Answers: apple, sandwich, banana, carrot, chips

Time to pack the food in Morgan's lunchbox. Will it all fit? Match the shape of each lunch food with the shape of the spaces in the lunchbox. Connect them with a line.

Which picture is different?

Answer: C

272

Time For Lunch!

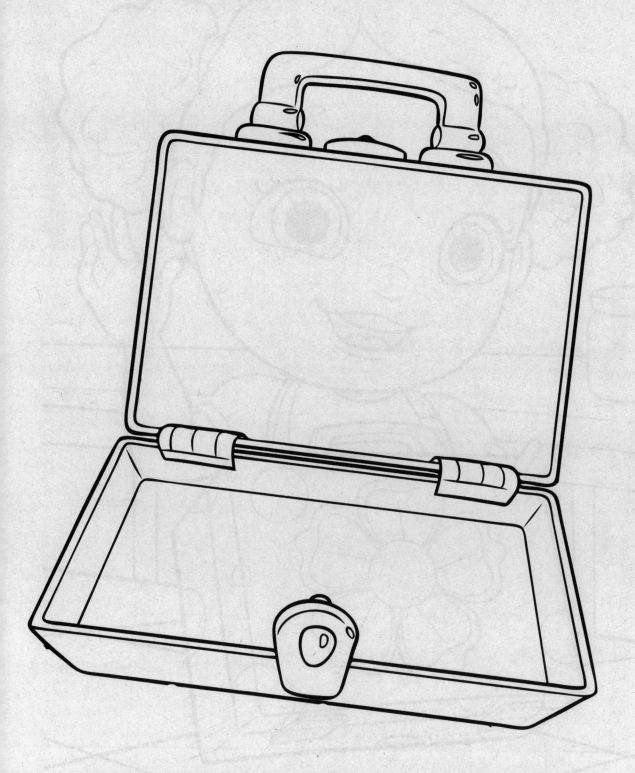

Fill up the lunchbox by drawing your favorite lunch foods.

© Disney

Thanks, Agent Oso! We did all 3 steps and got my lunch
ready for tomorrow before my bedtime.

Just doing my job. Now if you will excuse me, I have to get back to my Space Repair Training.

Morgan had to match shapes to pack her lunch.
That is exactly what I have to do, too. Match the shapes!

You did it, Agent Oso! Your training mission and your Special Assignment are complete. Way to go!

Goldflipper

Special Agent Oso is on a training mission.
He's learning to swim underwater.

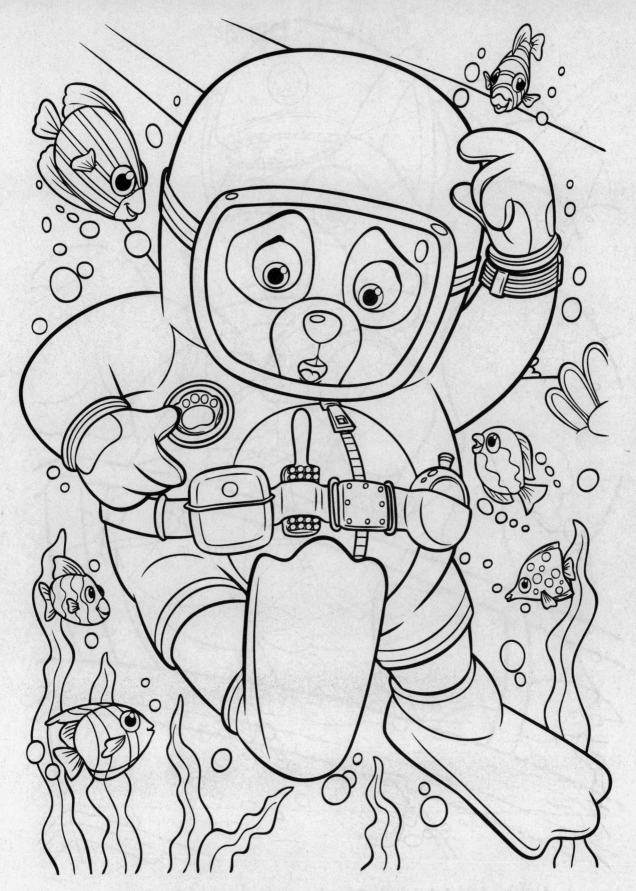

It's beautiful down here, but I can't seem
to move very fast.

Agent Wolfie told Agent Oso how to move fast underwater, but he can't remember what Wolfie said.

Help Agent Oso find his way back to Wolfie's spy boat.

© Disney

Zola has a goldfish. She won it at the school fair.
But she doesn't know how to care for her new pet.

Special Alert! Zola needs your help, Agent Oso!
You'll have to hurry. Her pet will need dinner soon.

Connect the dots.

Zola lives near the water. Wolfie's spy boat
will take Agent Oso there fast!

A school of fish. How many fish do you see?

Answer: 12

I'm here to help you learn how to care for your fish, Zola!

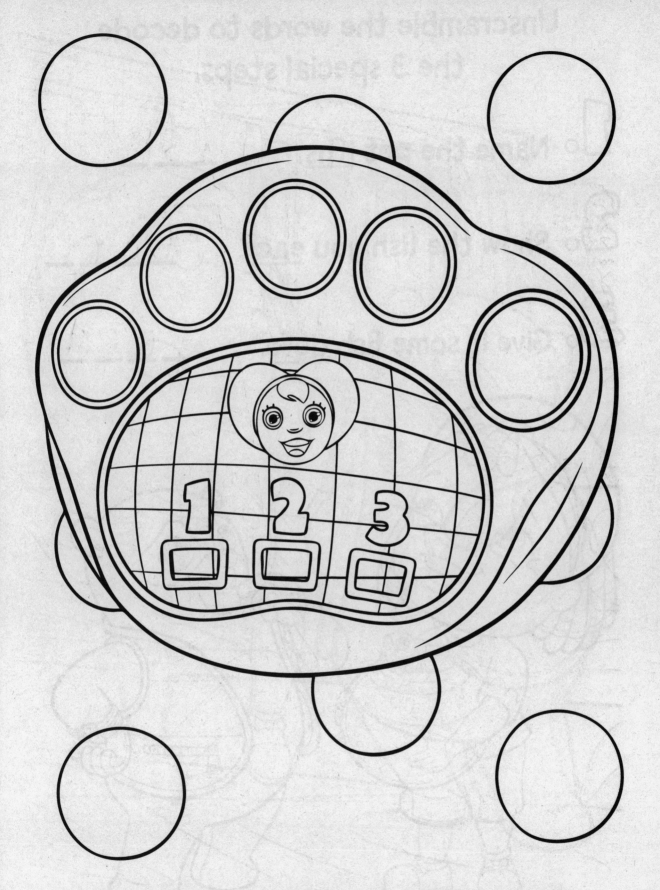

Your Special Assignment is starting now and
3 special steps will show you how!

Unscramble the words to decode the 3 special steps.

1. Name the pet <u>ifhs</u>.   <u>fish</u>

2. Show the fish you <u>eacr</u>.   <u>Care</u>

3. Give it some fish <u>dofo</u>.   <u>food</u>

Decorate the fishbowl with something special.
Ideas: a castle, plants, rocks.

Zola's pet is a goldfish that loves to do flips.
She'll call him Goldflipper!

Goldflipper is a great name, Agent Oso.
Now, help show Zola how to care for her goldfish!

© Disney

I'll decorate Goldflipper's fishbowl with bright stones and a castle. And I promise to keep his water nice and clean.

© Disney

What comes next in the pattern?
Fill in the blank.

1. 1231231 _23_

2. OSOSOS _OS_

3. 102S102 _S_

Answers: 2, O, S

Step 3. Give the fish some food, but not too much food! Food will keep the fish happy and healthy.

Draw the happy fish Agent Oso is thinking about.

© Disney

Find the fish food in the picture. Circle it.

Zola sprinkles just the right amount of
fish food into the fish bowl.

I did it! I learned how to care for my pet.
Goldflipper is so happy, he's flipping his flippers!

I have to get back to my training mission.
I just remembered what Wolfie told me.

Which picture is different?

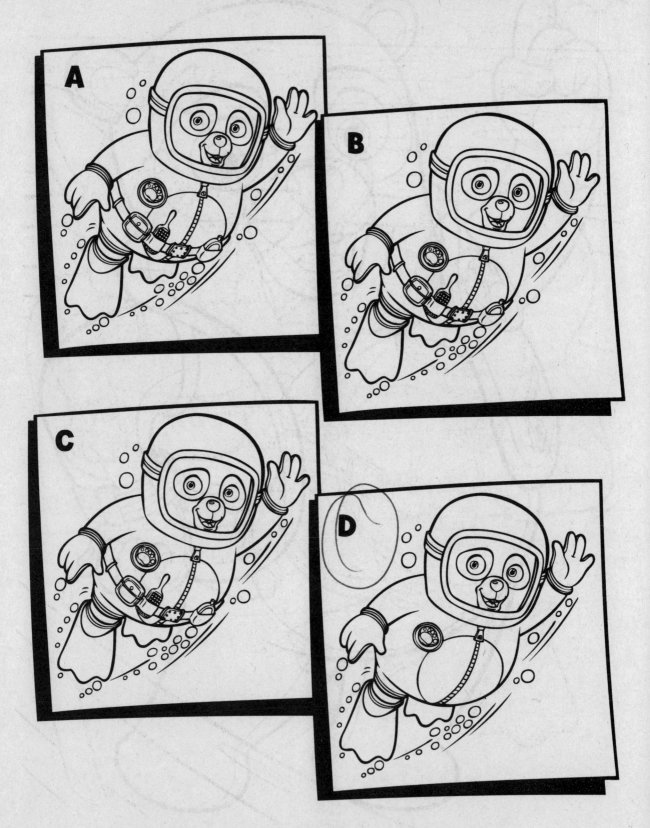

Wolfie said I should flip my flippers to move fast underwater!

Answer: D

You completed your training and your
Special Assignment, Agent Oso. Outstanding!

Your Special Assignment is complete.
This Digi-Medal is for you!

Which line leads to the Digi-Metal?

Your
Answer: ☐

Answer: 2

© Disney

Lemons are Forever

Agent Oso is learning Map Skills. He must find his way to
Agent Wolfie at UNIQUE headquarters.

© Disney

I must have missed a turn! Wolfie said I might get lost if I didn't do something. But I can't remember what it was!

Help Special Agent Oso find the road that leads to Wolfie.

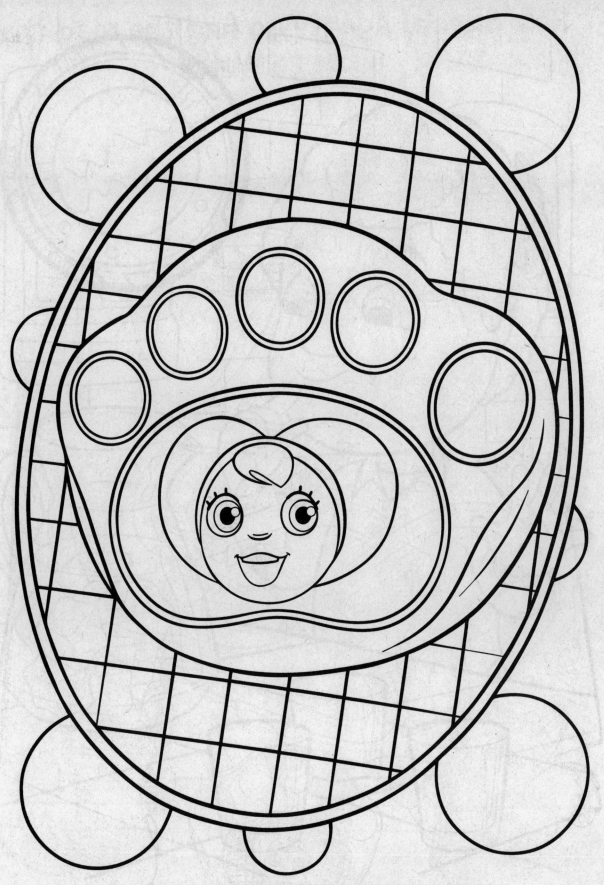

Special Alert! Special Alert! You have a
Special Assignment.

Hector's friends will soon be at his lemonade stand.
But Hector doesn't know how to make lemonade.

Let's Make Lemonade!
Count the number of glasses you see below.

Your Answer: 11

© Disney

Will you help me with this Special Assignment?

Agent Oso must follow 3 special steps to complete the assignment. Can you put the steps in order?

Number each step 1, 2 or 3.

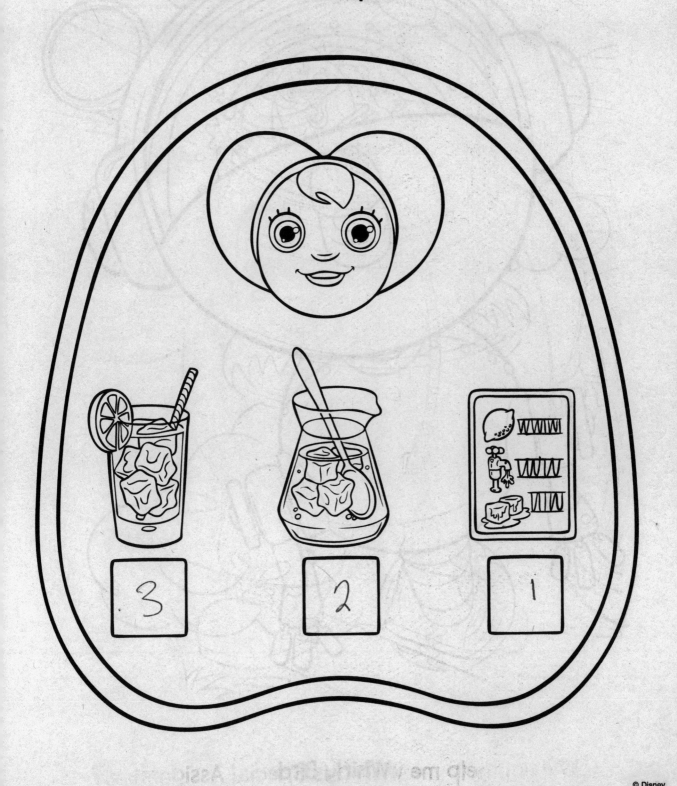

Whirly Bird

Agent Oso parachutes into Hector's yard.
It's all part of the plan!

Draw a line connecting the two identical pictures of Special Agent Oso.

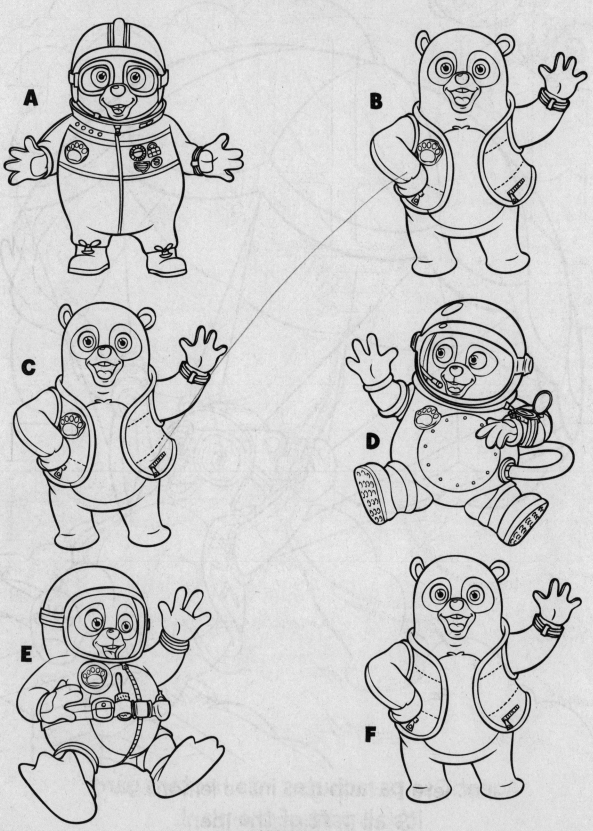

© Disney

I'm here to help you make lemonade.
Step 1: Find a recipe.

© Disney

Count the lemons not in the bowl and then color in the correct number.

5 6 7 8 9

Answer: 9

314

Mister Dos loves lemonade. He gave me this recipe!

Mister Dos's
Lemonade

4 Lemons, juiced
4 Cups water
1 Cup sugar
Pour over ice
and stir.

© Disney

Draw more lemons and ice in the pitcher!

Which line leads to Paw Pilot?

Your Answer: ☐

Answer: 1

Everything is ready. Careful, Agent Oso!

Step 2: Mix everything together.
Circle the 4 things you need to make lemonade.

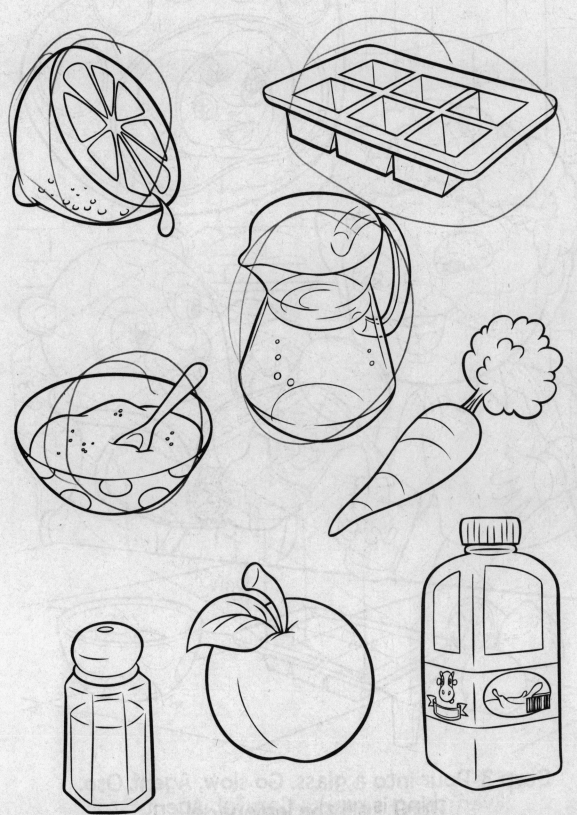

Step 3: Pour into a glass. Go slow, Agent Oso.
Don't spill the lemonade!

The lemonade is ready in time. It tastes great!

© Disney

Find 5 things that have been added to the bottom picture and circle them.

Answers: rake, key, lemon, shoe, book

Just doing my job! Now I have to get back
to my training exercise.

Hector helped me remember what Wolfie said. He told me to "go slow" or I might miss the turn!

There it is! That's the way back to headquarters.
Going slow helped me find the right road!

Agent Oso, you've completed your mission and earned this Map Skills Digi-Medal. Congratulations!

This Digi-Medal is for you! Connect the dots beginning with number 1 to complete your Digi-Medal.

© Disney

From Kai, With Love

Special Agent Oso is climbing a skyscraper.
He has suction cups on his shoes!

© Disney

Agent Dotty said these suction cups would hold me to the wall. It's part of my Wall-Walking Training.

© Disney

Which picture is different?

Your Answer:

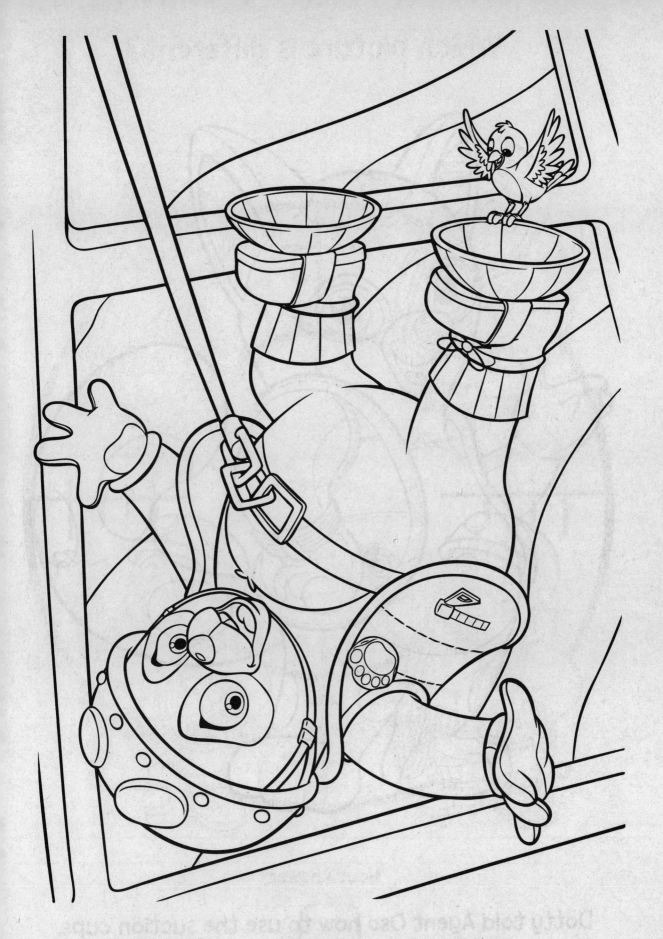

It's all part of the plan. More or less.

© Disney

Dotty told Agent Oso how to use the suction cups.
He just can't remember what she said.

Draw what you think Agent Oso is thinking about.
Hang on, Oso!

© Disney

Kai's sister Mei is having a birthday party.
Kai made her a present. It's a picture frame.
But he doesn't know how to wrap it!

© Disney

Shutter Bug is on the case.

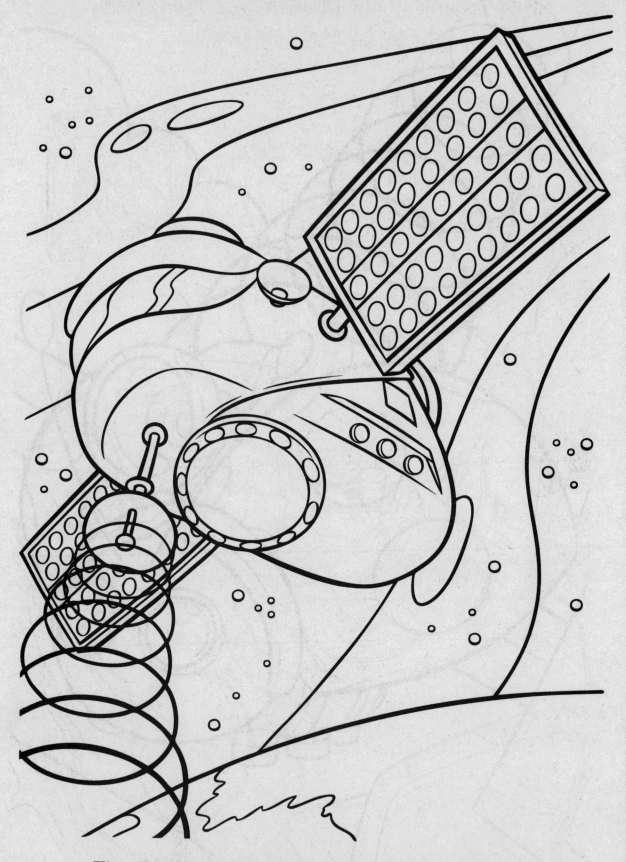

The Tracking Satellite receives the signal.
A special alert goes out to Agent Oso!

Find 7 items in the picture that start with the letter P. Circle them.

Answers: 1-presents, 2-plates, 3-party hats, 4-pitcher, 5-punch, 6-picture, 7-piñata

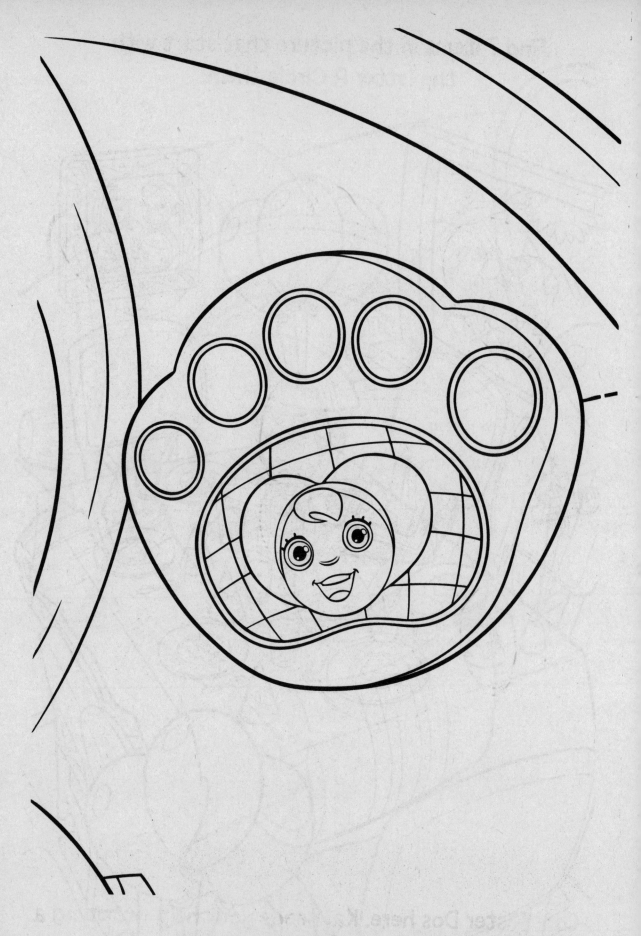

Special Alert! Special Alert!

Oso! Mister Dos here. Kai needs your help wrapping a present! You'll have to hurry. The party will begin soon.

What Time Is It?
Morgan's party starts at 4 o'clock.
Which watch has the correct time?

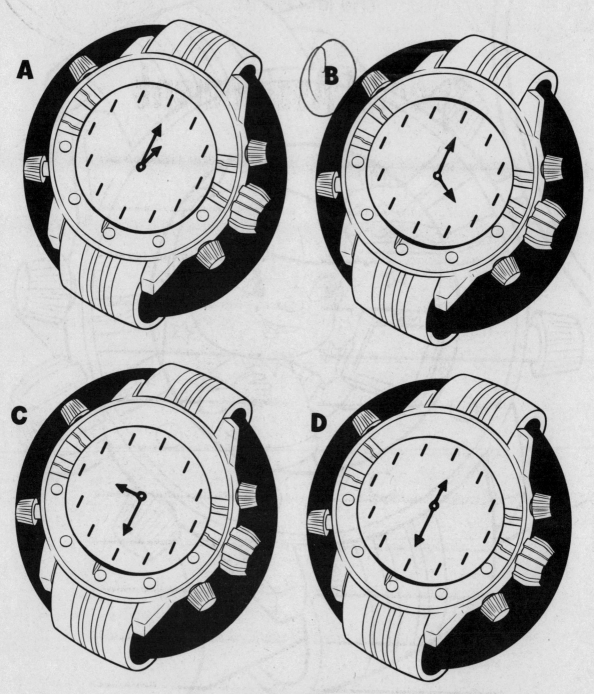

A

B

C

D

Your Answer:

Answer: B

340

How many words can you make using the letters in:

Special Assignment

_____   _____

_____   _____

_____   _____

_____   _____

_____   _____

_____   _____

_____   _____

_____   _____

_____   _____

Use the grid to draw Paw Pilot.

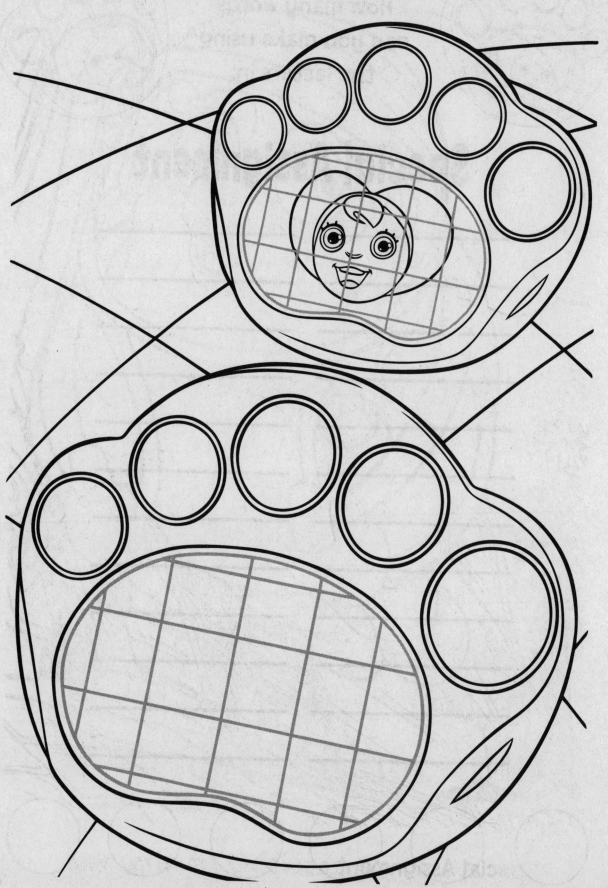

Special Assignment accepted. I'm on my way!

Circle the three things Agent Oso needs to wrap the present.

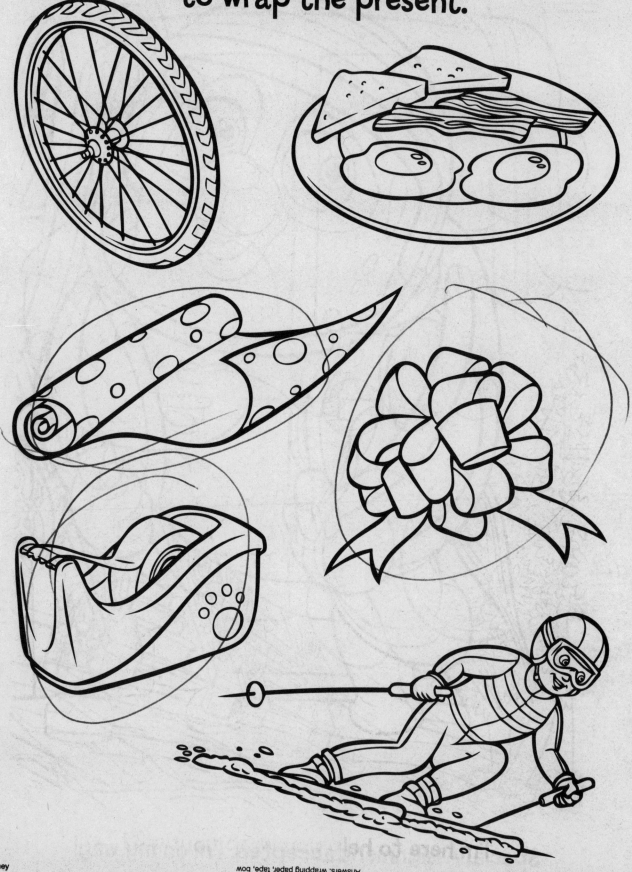

I'm here to help you wrap your gift!

Your gift will look just as nice as these.
Can you find some wrapping paper?
That is step 1.

I found it! The wrapping paper was in the closet.

Help Agent Oso by finding the tape hidden in the picture. Circle it. Then, find and circle 6 more items that don't belong on Kai's toy shelf.

Answers: fork, cup and saucer, rake, hairbrush, spaghetti, bowtie

Step 2 is to use tape.
Agent Oso is tangled up in the tape. It's a sticky situation!

Hurry, Oso! Step 3 is to add a bow. Press it down firmly.

That's it! Dotty told me to press
the suction cups down firmly!

Which picture is different?

Excuse me, but I have to get back to my Wall-Walking.

© Disney

Special Assignment complete! Unscramble the words.

FTIG gifT

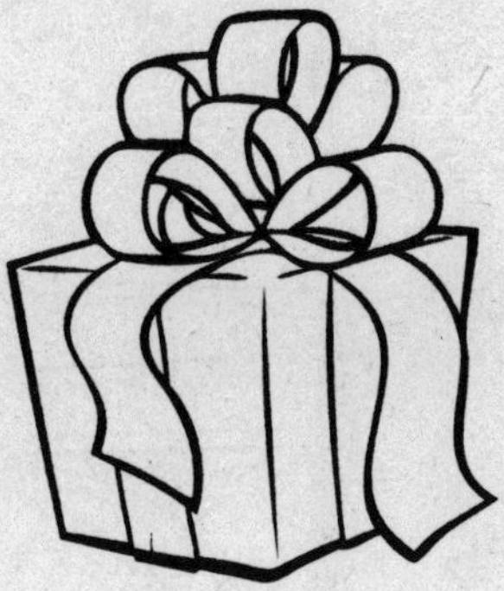

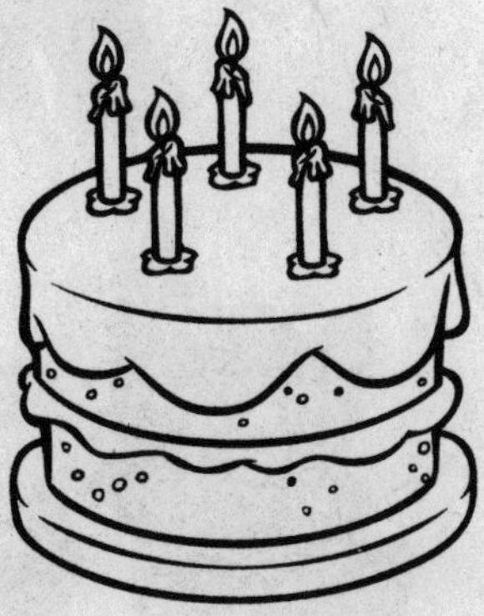

 ACKE CAKE

ATH HAT

 NDACEL candel

NLOLABO Balloon

Answers: gift, cake, hat, candle, balloon.

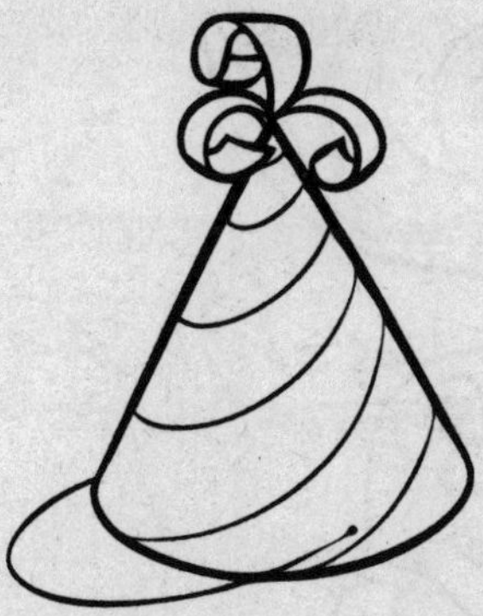

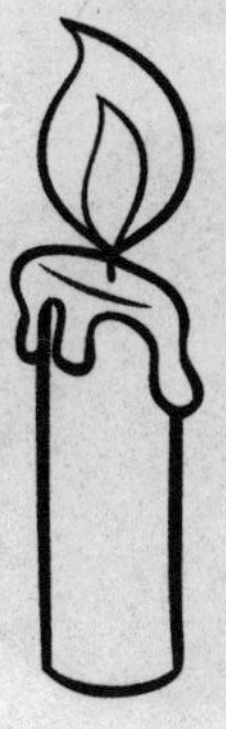

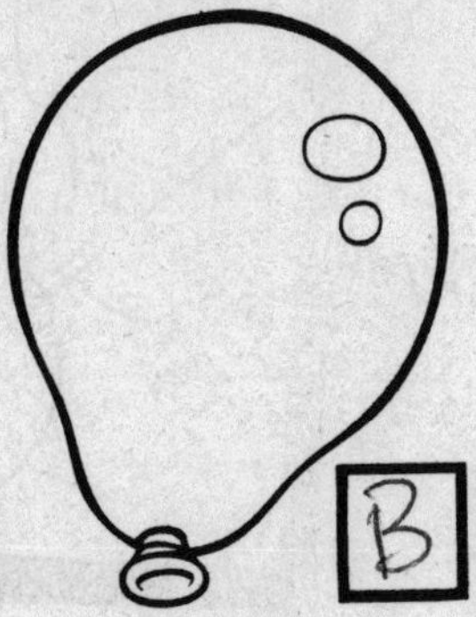

Match the shadows.

© Disney

354

Draw the present in the grid.

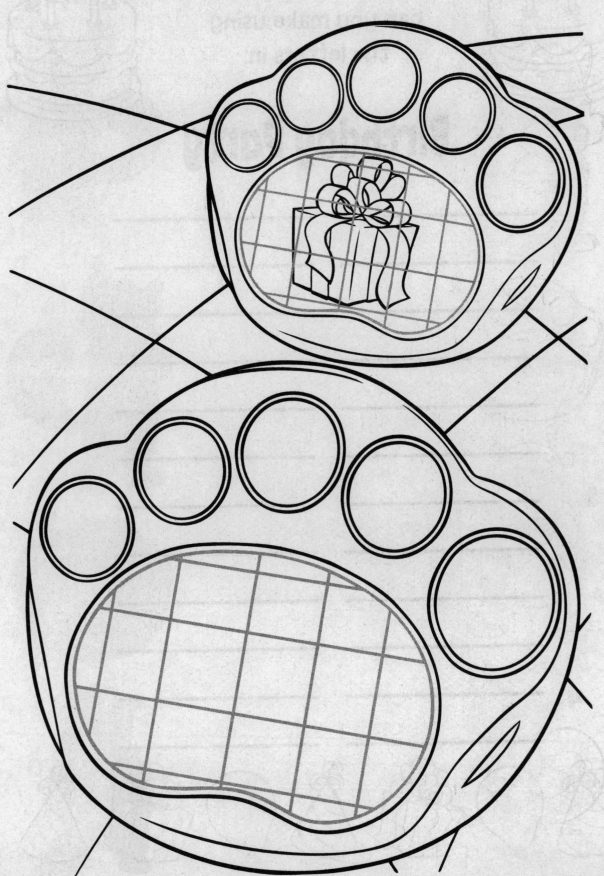

How many words can you make using the letters in:

Birthday Party

_____   _____

_____   _____

_____   _____

_____   _____

_____   _____

_____   _____

_____   _____

_____   _____

_____   _____

_____   _____

It's Your Party!
Color the number of candles
you will need on your cake this year!

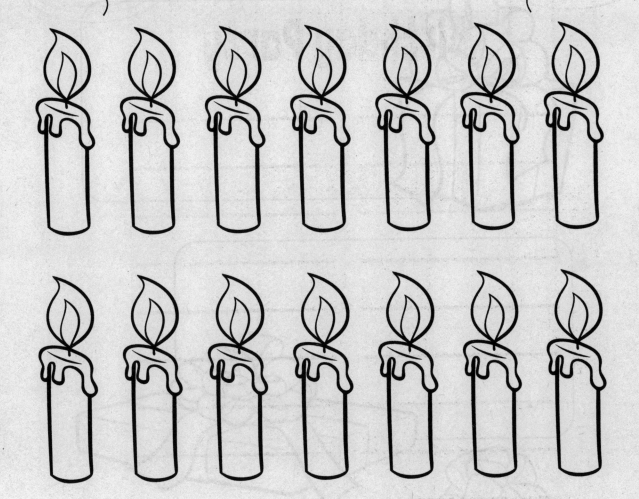

Your
Age:

Time For Presents!

Presents come in all sorts of shapes and sizes. Draw what you think Mei could receive in each of these gifts.

Happy Birthday, Mei!

Your Special Assignment is complete.
This Digi-Medal is for you!

The Never Land Pirates are having a dance party!

Captain Hook tries to spoil their fun!

The music reaches the Jolly Roger.

Mr. Smee dances to the beat.

"Mister Smee! Who's making that rat-a-tat racket?"

"It's the sea pups, Captain. They're dancing!"

© Disney

Captain Hook spots the happy
crew through his spyglass.

"This is an outrage," sneers Hook.
"We must put an end to their fun!"

"Excuse me. May I join your little party?"

"Ahoy, Captain Hook."

Go, Cubby, go!

"Great playing, Cubby! You earned 3 Gold Doubloons!"

"My, my. What fun bangy things!"

"Run, Smee!" cries Captain Hook.

"We can't let Hook spoil our fun.
Yo ho, let's go!"

"Play me a waltz, Smee," orders Captain Hook.

"Stop!" yells Hook. "That crashing
and clanging is too much!"

"Avast!" says Jake. "Give us our drums back!"

"Grab those pesky pirates!" shouts Hook.

"We need a pinch of pixie dust!"

"We got our drums and earned 3 Gold Doubloons!
Let's grab 'em and go!"

Look what washed ashore!

"It's an underwater diving helmet!" says Izzy.

"I spy treasure!" says Captain Hook. "I want to spoil their fun, so I must have that hat-buckety thing."

Cubby is going to look at the fish.

Cubby walks under the water.

"Aha! I've got it! The treasure is mine!"

"Aw, coconuts!" says Cubby.

"The scallywags are headed for Seahorse Shallows!"
squawks Skully.

"Look alive, crew! Yo ho, let's go!"

Captain Hook is underwater
looking at the seahorses.

Bucky can't get close to the shore.
The water is too shallow.

"Follow me, mateys!" yells Izzy. They swing on ropes
off the ship to the beach.

"We solved a Pirate Problem by getting to the beach and got 4 Gold Doubloons! Let's grab 'em and go!"

"I'm keeping the hat-bucket thingy!" says Hook.

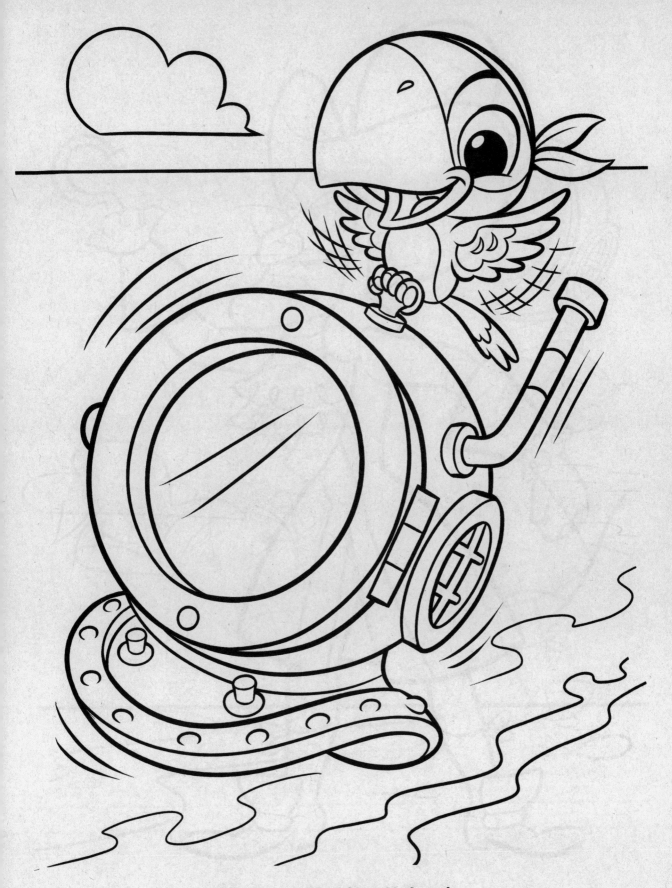

Skully grabs the helmet.
"Cheese and crackers! I've got it!"

"Barnacles!"

"This is all your fault, Smee!" says Hook.

© Disney

"Back to Pirate Island, me hearties!"